LifeTimes

The Story of Ludwig van Beethoven

by Stewart Ross

illustrated by Rob McCaig

Belitha Press

First published in the UK in 2002 by

Belitha Press Ltd
An imprint of Chrysalis Books plc
64 Brewery Road, London N7 9NT

Produced for Belitha Press by
White-Thomson Publishing Ltd
2/3 St Andrew's Place
Lewes, BN7 1UP

ISBN 1 84138 393 7

British Library Cataloguing in Publication Data for this book is available from the British Library.

Editor: Kay Barnham
Designer: John Jamieson
Language consultant: Norah Granger, Senior Lecturer in Primary
  Education at the University of Brighton.
Music consultant: Roland Vernon.

Printed in China

Introduction

Ludwig van Beethoven was born in Bonn,
Germany on 16 December 1770. His mother,
Maria Magdalena, and his father, Johann
(a singer and violinist), encouraged Ludwig
to become a musician. He gave his first public
concert when he was only seven years old.

In 1787, Ludwig travelled to Vienna and met
Mozart, a famous composer, who was very
impressed with him. Four years later, another
famous composer called Haydn invited
Ludwig back to Vienna to study with him.

Gradually, his reputation grew, until, on
2 April 1800, Ludwig van Beethoven hired
a hall, sold tickets and put on his first major
public concert…

'A Real Genius'

Ludwig stepped out before the orchestra and raised his hands. Gradually, the Royal Imperial Court Theatre fell silent. He gritted his teeth. This was it. The biggest test of his life so far.

The audience had applauded Ludwig's piano concerto. They had liked his chamber music, too. But would they approve of his symphony? In style it was quite like the Haydn and Mozart pieces that had been played earlier. Yet this was different – less bouncy, more romantic.

Ludwig paused for an instant. If the audience didn't like his symphony, all the hours, days and weeks he had slaved over the work would be in vain. All the money he had spent hiring the concert hall would be wasted. He would be a failure.

Putting such thoughts behind him, Ludwig nodded towards the orchestra, smiled and brought his right hand sharply down as a signal to them to start. Ludwig van Beethoven's *First Symphony* had begun.

Ludwig need not have worried. As the music ended, the audience broke into loud applause. The composer turned and bowed. A gentleman in the stalls waved his arms wildly. 'Bravo!' he shouted. 'Brilliant, Ludwig!' It was Ludwig's lively young brother. The composer smiled. Trust Nikky to make an exhibition of himself!

Later, when most of the audience had left, Ludwig was still surrounded by friends and well-wishers. Nikolaus was there, as was his other brother, Caspar.

In the crowd, a tall man with a wispy beard was explaining how he too had written a symphony… Ludwig stopped listening.

His attention had been caught by a couple on his left.

'Yes, it really was interesting!' said the woman.

'It was not just interesting,' exclaimed her husband. 'That van Beethoven is a genius – a real genius. One day he'll amaze the world!'

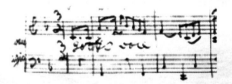

The Beethovens were a musical family. Ludwig's grandfather was a member of the Archbishop of Cologne's choir in Bonn. Ludwig's father, Johann, sang in the same choir. He and his wife Maria Magdalena had six children. Only Ludwig, the red-headed Caspar (born in 1774) and Nikolaus (born in 1776) survived. Ludwig was the most talented of the three. His father put pressure on his son to do well. He wanted Ludwig to tour Europe, making as much money as Mozart. Johann van Beethoven was disappointed when this did not happen.

The Old Fear

Ludwig woke late the next morning. For a while he lay in bed, thinking of the previous night's concert. He closed his eyes to imagine the scene again: the clapping, the shouts, the congratulations... It had all been so wonderful!

After dressing, Ludwig left his rooms on the third floor of 241 Tiefen Grabenat in Vienna and went out into the street. The bright spring morning added to his joyful mood. He had not believed life could be so good.

Half an hour later, refreshed by coffee and one of his favourite pastries, Ludwig climbed back to his rooms. He could not wait to get to his desk. An idea – partly a tune, partly a theme – had been buzzing around in his head for days. Ludwig felt the music bursting within him. He needed to let it out, to compose.

Ludwig covered two sheets of music, then glanced back over what he had written. Suddenly, he felt uneasy. He knew how others would hear his music. But what would it sound like to his own ears?

Like a monster looming out of the darkness, his old fear returned. Ludwig had been worried about his hearing for some time. Year after year, it had been getting worse. For a musician, this was the cruellest illness. Ludwig's greatest worry was that one day he would be unable to hear his own music.

In the last few
years, he had started
hearing strange buzzing
noises in his ears.
Ludwig had gone
to see a doctor.
The man poured oil
into his ears and said
that he would be better
within a fortnight.

But the treatment
seemed to make Ludwig's hearing worse,
not better. He had tried other doctors, but
without success. The buzzing did not go away
and now he found quiet sounds difficult
to hear.

Ludwig could write no more. Fear of
deafness seemed to freeze his hand. His ideas
dried up. In despair, he threw down his pen
and went out.

This time, he decided, whatever the cost,
he would go to the best doctor in Vienna.

Doctor Peter Frank, the director of the Vienna
Hospital, recognized the wild-looking Ludwig
at once. He invited the composer into his
private office.

'I hear your concert last night was a
triumph, Mr van Beethoven,' Frank said as
soon as the door was shut. 'Congratulations!'

'Thank you,' said Ludwig. 'You are very
kind. But I have not come about that.'

Frank nodded. 'Of course not. What can I
do for you?'

'Can you keep a secret?' Ludwig asked, looking nervous.

'Of course,' said the doctor. 'What is it?'

Ludwig scratched his head, twisted his fingers and looked uncomfortable. At last, he blurted out, 'I'm going deaf, doctor! And it's driving me mad!'

Dr Frank smiled. Ludwig would not go deaf, he promised, and he certainly would not go mad. All he needed were daily warm baths in water from the River Danube and herbal drops for his ears.

Ludwig thanked the doctor, paid him and followed his instructions carefully. The drops stung his ears. The warm baths were pleasant. But neither made any difference to his hearing. Once again, he was close to despair.

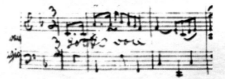

Beethoven was rarely in good health. He frequently suffered from stomach upsets that lasted for months. His deafness, however, was far more serious. It began as a constant noise in the ears – now known as 'tinnitus'. As time went on, Beethoven became unable to hear high-pitched sounds. The doctors of the day had no real idea what to do. None of the treatments they suggested did any good at all.

Secret Despair

The composer's
mood changed when a
famous horn player, Johann Wenzel
Stich, arrived in Vienna. Known as 'Punto', he
was the opposite of Ludwig – cheery, careless
and happy-go-lucky. Punto went to Ludwig
and asked him to play with him in a concert.

Ludwig's misery lifted like mist in the
morning. 'I will do more than play with you,
Punto!' he cried. 'I'll write a brand new piece
for us to perform.'

Punto booked a concert hall at once and announced an exciting programme. It included 'a new sonata for horn and piano by Ludwig van Beethoven'. Tickets sold well.

Four days before the concert, Punto called on Ludwig to go over the new sonata. He found the 30-year-old composer sitting at his desk, looking wilder than ever.

'Have you finished the piece?' Punto asked.

Ludwig swung round in his chair. 'Peas?' he asked. 'Why do you care what I eat, Punto?'

Punto laughed. 'My dear Ludwig! I said "piece", not "peas". I was asking about the sonata. Are you deaf or something?'

Ludwig looked deeply embarrassed. 'Of course I'm not going deaf!' he muttered. 'What use is a deaf musician to anyone?'

Punto looked at him carefully. Poor Ludwig was a brilliant musician, but a terrible liar.

Ludwig finished the sonata the night before the concert. Even then, he did not write out all of the piano part. He kept the themes in his head and made up the variations during the concert itself.

Once again, Ludwig's music was well received. Punto was delighted with the new sonata. He was due to play in the birthday concert of Archduchess Maria of Hungary and suggested that Ludwig accompany him to Budapest and play the piece there.

Ludwig immediately agreed. He needed to get out of Vienna for a while.

It would help his career, too, to play in Budapest, one of the great cities of the Austrian Empire.

Also, Ludwig thought, he would be able to call on his wealthy Hungarian friend, Count Franz Brunsvik. The count's lively young daughters, Josephine and Thérèse, were bound to want piano lessons.

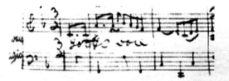

The Romantic movement in the arts (painting, music, literature, etc.) lasted from about 1770 to 1830. It stressed the importance of inner feelings, nature and the imagination. In music, Beethoven was at the head of this movement. The music he wrote after arriving in Vienna moved further and further from the formal, ordered style of his mentors, Haydn and Mozart.

The Great Romantic

Ludwig and Punto travelled to Budapest by coach. On the journey, the two men discussed their work. Ludwig said he was planning a new piano concerto. 'It will be different from anything else I have written,' he explained.

'How different?' asked Punto.

'It will have more of *me* in it,' replied Ludwig. 'More of my heart, more imagination.'

Punto grinned. 'More of you in it, Ludwig? Are you sure that's what people want?'

Ludwig stared out of the window at the green spring countryside. 'I have to obey my heart,' he said slowly, 'not what other people want. That is the way of a true artist.'

Punto disagreed. 'A true artist has to make a living,' he said. 'And that means giving the audience what they want.'

'I don't care!' shouted Ludwig angrily. 'The heart comes first – the rest is mud!'

Punto decided to let the matter drop.

Ludwig's *Sonata for Horn and Piano* was played on 7 May, the last day of Archduchess Maria's birthday celebrations. Before this concert, Ludwig had not been well known in Budapest. The sonata made the citizens eager to hear more of his music. After the concert, Punto continued his travels round Europe. He had had enough of Ludwig – the composer was too serious and much too quick to fly into a rage. And Ludwig was tired of Punto's light-hearted manner.

Ludwig went to visit the Brunsviks on their estate outside Budapest. The count was delighted to see him again and offered a room where he could compose in peace and quiet.

'In return, my dear Ludwig, I make only one request,' he said.

'And what is that, sir?' asked the composer.

'That you give piano lessons to my daughters, Josephine and Thérèse.'

Ludwig's heart jumped. This was what he had hoped for. 'Nothing, sir, would give me greater pleasure,' he replied seriously.

Ludwig stayed with his friends the Brunsviks until late July. Every day he worked long hours on his new piano concerto, writing and re-writing each section until he felt it was perfect. He never paid much attention to his clothes, and when he was working he looked as shabby as a scarecrow. His long hair stood on end, his shirt came unbuttoned and his jacket was a mass of creases.

Ludwig's appearance did not endear him to the Brunsvik girls. Short and thick set, with a pock-marked face, he was not handsome. When in the middle of  writing a piece of music, he often looked like an escaped convict who had been hiding in the woods for months.

So when Ludwig said, first to Josephine, then to Thérèse, that he thought he might fall in love with them, the two girls politely refused him.

'Romance,' explained Thérèse tactfully, 'would spoil our lovely friendship.'

Ludwig was no longer a young man and he very much wanted to get married. He was, therefore, upset when both Josephine and Thérèse turned him down. But, just before he left Hungary, they raised his hopes again.

'You remember our cousin, Countess Giulietta Guicciardi?' Josephine asked one evening at dinner.

Ludwig smiled. How could he forget the pretty countess he had once met in Vienna?

'Well,' continued Josephine, 'she is back in Vienna again. She wants a piano teacher, so I've written to her recommending you. You'll like Giulietta, Ludwig. She's grown up now, intelligent – and very pretty.'

Later, Ludwig went for a walk in the gardens alone. It was a beautiful night, still and starlit. As he watched the moon rising slowly over the distant fields, a ghost of a tune flitted into his mind.

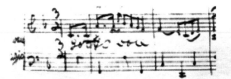

Beethoven had mastered a number of musical instruments, but his favourite was the piano. The instrument was developed from the harpsichord in Italy in the early eighteenth century. Its full name, 'pianoforte', means 'soft-loud'. Unlike a harpsichord player, a pianist can play loud and soft notes by touch. This made Beethoven's remarkable piano playing and compositions all the more fresh and exciting.

Master and Pupil

Back in Vienna, Ludwig finished his piano
concerto and pressed ahead with other pieces.
He lived on the money he received from
teaching and the annual 500 guilders from one
of his generous patrons, Count Lichnowsky.

Writing music did not automatically bring Ludwig money. Normally, a composition started earning when it was published and people bought the music to play for themselves. The only music that Ludwig published in 1800 was his *Six Easy Variations for the Pianoforte*.

Meanwhile, the musical theme that had first come to Ludwig in the Brunsviks' moonlit garden continued to grow. He had decided it would be a piano sonata, a personal one that captured the romance in his soul. Whenever he worked on it, an image of the young Countess Giulietta floated before his eyes. But, although she was often in his thoughts, Ludwig was disappointed that he had not heard a word from her.

In 1801, Austria was at war with France. Ludwig was kept busy performing in charity concerts to raise money for wounded soldiers.

Then, two months later, he moved to rooms near the old city walls. For a time, cheered by the fresh air and magnificent views of Vienna, his health improved and he forgot about his increasing deafness.

The visit he had been expecting for so long came shortly after he had moved to his new home.

A servant of Count Guicciardi arrived. Would Mr van Beethoven accept his master's daughter, Giulietta, as a pupil on the pianoforte?

Ludwig hid his excitement, calmly replying that he could fit in one more pupil. The servant left, having arranged that the countess would come for her first lesson in two days' time. Ludwig always insisted that his pupils came to him. Only common tradesmen, he believed, took their wares to other people's houses.

With her wide, dark eyes and beautiful smile, Countess Giulietta was just as lovely as Ludwig remembered her. She was clever, too, and an able pianist. From her very first lesson, master and pupil struck up a powerful relationship.

Ludwig was not at all the ideal teacher. He was impatient. Sometimes, if his pupil failed to play a piece correctly, he would lose his temper and tear up the music they were studying.

On the other hand, able pupils learned a great deal just by watching the master at work.

The seventeen-year-old Giulietta recognized Ludwig's genius. She ignored his small size, his messy looks and his rough face. She even took no notice when, from time to time, he seemed not to hear what she said.

To her mind, all that mattered were the golden sounds that flowed from Ludwig's fingers, not his shabby appearance and awkward manner.

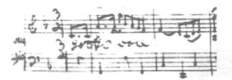

In Beethoven's time, a sonata was a piece of music for the solo piano or for another instrument accompanied by the piano. It was generally in three sections, called movements; the second movement was normally slower. Beethoven wrote 32 piano sonatas, including the famous *Moonlight Sonata*, which he dedicated to Giulietta Guicciardi. They are widely considered to be some of the finest pieces of piano music ever written. His variations on original themes are full of imagination and reflect his superb technical skill as a pianist.

The Moonlight Sonata

Ludwig was as fond of Giulietta as she was
of him. But he was too embarrassed to say so.
Once, as she was leaving with the maid
who always accompanied her, he spoke up.
'I'm sorry I'm not a good teacher, Countess
Giulietta. I'm hopeless with words. Music is
the only language I can speak.'

At home, Giulietta thought about what
Ludwig had said. At her next lesson, she asked,
'Mr van Beethoven, you know you said that
music is your only language?'

'Yes?' replied Ludwig.

'Well,' said Giulietta, 'would you tell me, in music, what you think of your pupil?'

Ludwig looked at her awkwardly. 'That is very difficult, Countess. Some things cannot be said, even in music. But I will try.'

Giulietta got up and moved to a chair on the other side of the room. Ludwig pulled his stool nearer the piano, paused for a moment, then began to play.

Ludwig played for fifteen minutes with hardly a pause. The piece, which was new to Giulietta, was the most beautiful music she had ever heard. When it was over, she sat in silence with tears running down her face.

Ludwig turned and looked at her. 'You liked my piece, Countess Giulietta?'

The girl wiped her eyes and smiled. 'Liked it? It's magical! Surely it is not really what you think of your pupil?'

Delighted by her reaction, Ludwig grinned and stood up. 'The idea for the first movement came to me one moonlit night,' said Ludwig.

'It was perfectly beautiful – so yes, it *is* what I think of my pupil.' A few minutes later, after Giulietta had sent her maid out of the room, Ludwig asked her if she would marry him. She agreed at once. But first, he had to get her father's permission.

Down but not Out

Ludwig had not expected the count's question. He explained that he was not rich, at least, not by the count's standards.

'Then will you be rich one day?' asked the count, slowly rocking back on his heels.

'I can't say,' answered Ludwig honestly. 'I have a mission to bring beautiful music to the world. It may make me rich, it may not. In the end, that's not important. What really matters is the music.'

'And what really matters to me,' replied the count, 'is my daughter's happiness. She has been raised in great comfort. Should I let her marry some musician – even a musical genius – who won't be able to afford medicine when she is ill? Who won't be able to send her children to school?'

'There will be love,' replied Ludwig firmly. 'And music.'

'Maybe,' said the count, equally firmly. 'But neither love nor music will pay the bills.'

In the end, the count refused to let Giulietta
marry Ludwig. He respected Ludwig, he said,
and he admired his music. But it was not the
best thing for his daughter – his future
prospects were unsure and he was from a
different social class. Besides, Giulietta was too
young to know what she was really doing.

'I'm very sorry. Mr van Beethoven,' the
count finished. 'But I'm sure another, more
suitable, young lady will turn up soon—'

Before the count could finish, Ludwig had run out of the room. He could not take any more. He was losing his hearing and now he had lost his Giulietta. What was the point of going on?

In despair, Ludwig hurried from the city and out into the countryside. After about an hour, he sat beside a stream and stared into the icy waters. A deaf musician! It was a joke. And a deaf, ugly, lonely musician was even more of a joke.

What should he do? Ludwig looked around at
the grassy meadow. Maybe he should stay here
and become a shepherd? Sitting alone in a field
all day, it wouldn't matter if he were deaf.

With a sigh, he lay back and gazed at the
mountains against the purple-blue evening sky.
They were so mighty, yet they too were deaf…

Ludwig remembered what he had overheard
at his concert: 'One day he'll amaze the world!'

That was it! Although his heart was broken,
although his hearing was fading fast, he must
not give up. Whatever the pain, he had to
create music that would amaze the world.

In Beethoven's day large-scale serious music was played by an orchestra. This consisted of four sections:

    1 Strings (such as violins and cellos);

    2 Woodwind instruments (such as flutes and clarinets);

    3 Brass (such as horns and trumpets);

    4 Percussion (such as drums and cymbals).

Beethoven experimented with the traditional roles given to the instruments. In his *Third Symphony*, for example, he gave the horns special importance. And he composed his famous *Ninth* (and last) *Symphony* for an orchestra and chorus.

Beethoven's Later Life

Although he had several women friends after Giulietta, Beethoven never married and had no children.

As he grew older and his hearing worsened, Beethoven became more depressed and difficult to get on with. Sadly, he died of pneumonia in 1827, when he was only 57.

Beethoven's Music

When he was refused permission to marry Giulietta in 1801, Beethoven's music was entering a new, exciting phase. Breaking away from old forms of music by Haydn and Mozart, he was creating a new style of music. It was tuneful, passionate and often thrilling to listen to. Some of the best examples are his *Fifth Symphony*, his *Fifth Piano Concerto* and the *Ninth (Choral) Symphony*. As he grew older, his music became more complicated. Even so, many experts believe his last string quartets are some of the finest pieces of music ever written.

Timeline

1770	16 December, Beethoven born in Bonn, Germany.
1778	Gives his first public recital.
1784	Composes a piano concerto.
1787	Meets Mozart in Vienna.
	Mother dies.
1792	Goes to live in Vienna.
	Taught by Haydn.
	Father dies.
1798	First signs of deafness.
1800	Completes his *First Symphony*.
1800	First concert.
1801	Finishes *Moonlight Sonata* for piano.
1805	First performance of *Third Symphony* (*Eroica*).
1808	Finishes *Sixth Symphony* (*Pastoral*).
1809	The French capture Vienna.
1810	First performance of *Fifth Piano Concerto*.
1815	Now almost totally deaf.
1817	Begins his *Ninth Symphony* (*Choral*).
1825-6	Works on his last quartets.
1827	26 March, dies in Vienna.

More Information

Books to read

Beethoven by Wendy Lynch, Heinemann, 2000.
Ludwig van Beethoven by Dynise Balcavage, Chelsea House, 1997.
Introducing Beethoven by Roland Vernon, Belitha Press, 2000.

Museums

Beethoven Memorial, Florisdorf, Vienna.
Beethoven House Museum, Bonn.

Websites

http://www.unitel.classicalmusic.com/uhilites/010100.htm
http://classicalmus.hispeed.com/articles/beethoven.html

You can hear Beethoven's music on:
http://www.classicalarchives.com

Glossary

archduchess Female equivalent of an archduke (the highest form of duke) or wife of an archduke.
chamber music Music normally played with no more than eight instruments.
compose To write music.
concerto Piece of music played by an orchestra and a solo instrument, such as a piano or violin.
count Nobleman.
countess Female equivalent of a count, or a count's wife.
guilder Coin used in the Netherlands.

quartet Piece of music played by four instruments.
solo Piece of music played on one instrument.
sonata Piece of music played by a piano or by another instrument accompanied by a piano.
stalls Seats at the front of a theatre.
symphony Large piece of music, usually divided into movements, played by an orchestra.
variations Different ways of playing a musical theme.

Index